MR BLOOD'S BODY LESSONS

Pickle Hill Primary

Mr Day's Knight Lessons
Phil Roxbee Cox

Mr Fossil's Dinosaur Lessons
Valerie Wilding

Miss Galaxy's Space Lessons
Phil Roxbee Cox

Mr Megamouth's Shark Lessons
Michael Cox

Miss Nile's Mummy Lessons
Alan MacDonald

Mrs Parrot's Rainforest Lessons
Michael Cox

Miss Scorcher's Desert Lessons
Valerie Wilding

PICKLE HILL PRIMARY
WHERE ANYTHING CAN HAPPEN

MR BLOOD'S
BODY
LESSONS

Michael Cox

illustrated by
Kelly Waldek

SCHOLASTIC

Scholastic Children's Books,
Commonwealth House, 1–19 New Oxford Street,
London WC1A 1NU, UK

A division of Scholastic Ltd
London ~ New York ~ Toronto ~ Sydney ~ Auckland
Mexico City ~ New Delhi ~ Hong Kong

Published in the UK by Scholastic Ltd, 2003

ISBN 0 439 97820 3

Typeset by M Rules
Printed and bound by Nørhaven Paperback, Viborg, Denmark

2 4 6 8 10 9 7 5 3 1

Contents

Welcome to ✷ Pickle Hill Primary ✷

Hello, my name's Laxmi Sharma and I go to Pickle Hill Primary School. Before you turn the page I think I probably ought to let you know that Pickle Hill has some very odd teachers who teach some very strange (but absolutely amazing!) lessons.

One of these teachers is Mr Blood. He's got some great ways of really getting <u>into</u> his subject. I won't tell you what they are now as you'll find out soon enough. All I will say is that during his body lessons all of us in class 5M got the <u>inside</u> story on ourselves and our friends... from top to bottom! And we all got to know ourselves much better!

So, if you've got the stomach for it (not to mention the heart, lungs and liver!) why not join me and the rest of class 5M for Mr Blood's extraordinary body lessons.

by Laxmi →

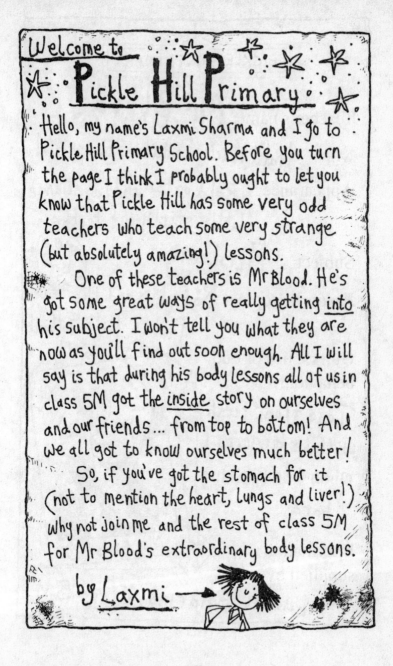

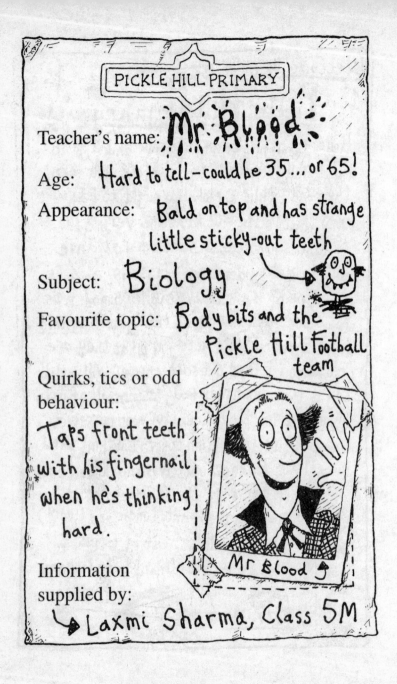

PICKLE HILL PRIMARY

Teacher's name: **Mr Blood**

Age: Hard to tell – could be 35... or 65!

Appearance: Bald on top and has strange little sticky-out teeth

Subject: Biology

Favourite topic: Body bits and the Pickle Hill Football team

Quirks, tics or odd behaviour:

Taps front teeth with his fingernail when he's thinking hard.

Mr Blood

Information supplied by: Laxmi Sharma, Class 5M

THIS IS MY CLASS 5M

Zoe Thompson

Liam O'Brady

Brian Butler

Simon Sidworth

Charlotte Edwards

Kelly Niblett

Daniel Matson

This is me! ➤

(Laxmi Sharma)

Under Brian's birthday suit

Last Monday, just after register, Mr Blood came into our classroom. He was pushing a big glass screen, which was surrounded by a blue plastic frame with lots of little dials and switches attached to it.

"Uh-oh!" whispered my best pal, Zoe Thompson. "Looks like we're in for fun and games today!"

"Er, what's that strange-looking machine, Mr Blood?" I asked.

"It's called an 'X-magnascope', Laxmi," said Mr Blood, fiddling with some sort of remote-control handset. "We're going to be learning all about our bodies so this gizmo is going to come in extremely useful. Now, first of all, I need a volunteer to help me demonstrate its terrific tricks."

"Me! Me!" shouted everyone in the class. (We're a very trusting bunch.)

Mr Blood looked thoughtful for a moment then said, "Well, as it's Brian Butler's birthday, I'll choose him. Come and stand just here please, Brian."

Brian did as he was told as Mr Blood wheeled the screen in front of him. And all of a sudden Brian was standing there in just his socks and underpants!

"Ah ha!" yelled Daniel Mapson, when we'd recovered from our shock. "It's Brian's birthday … and he's in his birthday suit!"

(You're right, Daniel's our class clown.)

"Now I'll zoom in so we can get a closer look at Brian's *birthday* suit!" said Mr Blood. "And Kelly and Charlotte, will you please stop that vulgar whistling and hooting!"

Mr Blood gave the X-magnascope's handset a swift tweak and this is what we saw:

CLOSE UP × 5

Brian's birthday suit (or skin as most people call it) magnified × 5

Jobs: regulates body temperature → HOT WARM COLD

germs → keeps out germs

BRIAN'S GOT ABOUT 1.5 SQUARE METRES OF SKIN. IT'S DRY, STRETCHY AND WATERPROOF. WEIGHING ABOUT THREE KILOGRAMS, IT'S HEAVIER THAN ANY OTHER PART OF HIS BODY.

little sweat holes (pores)

tiny hairs screen scalp from sun...

...help sense of touch...

...and keep head warm in winter

BRIAN CHANGES HIS SKIN COMPLETELY ABOUT EVERY THREE WEEKS.

"Does he peel it off and hang it up in his wardrobe?" joked Daniel.

"Actually," Mr Blood explained, "Brian is constantly shedding billions and billions of tiny, tiny bits of skin every time he washes, walks, turns over in bed or simply rubs himself against a brick wall in the school playground when he wants a good scratch. During our lifetime we all lose about 50 kilograms of dead skin by doing these various things."

"By the way," said Mr Blood, pointing at the screen, "every one of these hairs has its own little muscle!"

"Aaaah!" said Kelly Niblett. (She's very sentimental.)

HAIR by Kelly

We have hair all over our bodies apart from our lips, palms and the soles of our feet.

← hairs →

oil (keeps our hair soft and shiny)

gland (tiny oil squirter)

follicles (little pouches)

You lose between 50 and 100 hairs every day (unless you're Mr Blood who hasn't got much left to lose).

Brilliant little muscles make our hairs stand up when we are cold to trap warm air between the hairs.

NORTH POLE

SKIN COLOUR by Laxmi

Stuff called melanin gives your skin its colour. My skin is brown because my family come from India where there's tons more sunshine than in the UK. Melanin has made our skin darker to protect us from the sun's harmful rays. This happens to everyone. The sunnier it is, the darker your skin is.

Kelly's got freckles because there are bits of her skin where there is more melanin.

"Now," said Mr Blood, twiddling the controls on the X-magnascope. "We'll go just a little bit deeper."

DERMIS...

amazing vast, all-over, built-in alarm system equipped with:
pressure sensors
heat sensors
cold sensors
pain sensors

15

"What you saw a moment ago was Brian's outer skin, or epidermis as it's known. We are now looking at Brian's under-skin, or dermis," Mr Blood explained. "There are sensors in his dermis that can immediately send pain messages along the nerves in his spine to his brain, warning him that he is in danger."

SUPER SKIN ALARM SYSTEM by Daniel

If you touch a red-hot plate... OW! Zzzz! ssss!

...stab yourself with a sharp pencil... EEK!

...or accidentally fall into a huge barrel of kumquat-flavoured ice lollies... YIKES! SHIVER SHIVER!

...Sensors under your skin (dermis) let you know.

"Oh, I get it!" I said. "If we didn't feel pain, we'd soon burn, freeze or bash ourselves to bits!"

"Exactly, Laxmi," said Mr Blood.

He gave his front teeth a couple of swift taps, then said, "I think we'll give X-magnascope's depth modulator another tweak and go even deeper."

He twiddled the remote control again and now Brian's *skin* disappeared! But fortunately, his underpants stayed in place!

"Uuurgh, yuk!" groaned Daniel as everyone gazed in amazement at the gruesome red and pink Brian that had just appeared behind the screen.

"This is more or less what all of us look like under our skin," smiled Mr Blood. "Beauty really is only skin-deep."

Then he flicked the remote control and said, "OK! Time to zoooooom again!"

"Now we're looking at just one little bit of Brian magnified about 20,000 times," said Mr Blood.

"What are all those little red and pink and yellow things?" I asked. "They look a bit like Bombay mix to me."

"What you are looking at is a cluster of Brian's body cells," said Mr Blood. "That's what he's made up of."

"What?" said Daniel. "*All* of him?"

"Yes," said Mr Blood. "Our Brian here is nothing more than a huge mass of cells."

"Ah, poor thing," said Kelly, suddenly looking like she felt really sorry for Brian. "Can't anyone do anything to help him?"

"It's all right, Kelly," said Mr Blood. "It's perfectly normal. All living things are made from cells. They're like those plastic bricks you can build into any shape you want. Except our cells are almost all living … and always busy, busy, busy! Altogether, you've got about 200 different sorts of cell and each type has its own job. Everything to do with being alive takes place inside our body cells."

"But what about things like our bones and eyeballs and hair and chins and lips?" asked Zoe. "Are they made of these cell things too?"

"They are," said Mr Blood. "Any living thing you care to think of is built from cells."

"Plus bananas, blackberry bushes, blue whales and baboons!" yelled Simon Sidworth.

"All of those too!" laughed Mr Blood.

"And *Brian Butlers*!" said Brian, looking really pleased with himself.

"Exactly!" said Mr Blood. "And does anyone know where this mass of cells that we know as Brian Butler came from?"

"15 Oaktree Crescent!" shouted Daniel Mapson.

"No," said Mr Blood. "Our Brian came from one single cell."

"Cripes!" said Zoe. "He must have been *really* tiny!"

"And really *lonely*!" said Kelly, giving Brian a sympathetic smile.

"He *was* tiny," said Mr Blood. "Smaller than a pinhead. Look I'll show you."

And with that he flicked a switch on the X-magnascope and announced, "Brian Butler, this is your life. Well, a bit of it anyway!"

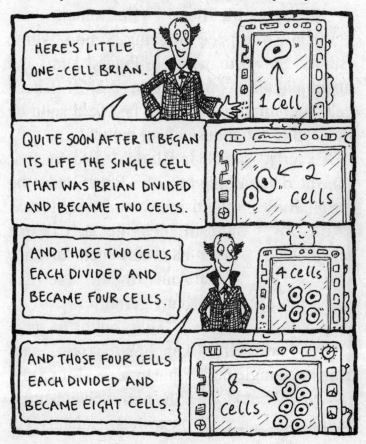

"While Brian was still inside his mum, his body cells kept on dividing and increasing in number to make stuff called tissue," continued Mr Blood as he paused the video.

"Tissue?" said Kelly, looking bewildered.

"Yes, Kelly," said Mr Blood. "That's right. Tissue!"

"Bless you, Mr Blood!" said Daniel.

When we stopped laughing, Simon "Three Brains" Sidworth, who's brilliant at sums and about ten billion other things, said, "If Brian's cells were multiplying that fast he'd soon be thousands and thousands of cells!"

"Exactly," said Mr Blood. "And by that time he'd be starting to look a little bit like the Brian Butler we all know and love today.

Except he still didn't have any teeth or hair. And was the size of a baby gerbil."

"They ought to have kept him that way," said Charlotte Edwards. (She hasn't been getting on with Brian lately!)

"I don't remember any of this," said Brian.

"You wouldn't," said Mr Blood. "Your brain and memory were nowhere near fully developed at that time."

"Still aren't, if you ask me," muttered Charlotte.

"*I'm* actually made of about 75 billion cells," said Mr Blood. "Give or take a few flakes of dead skin and the odd stray hair. However, you lot are not nearly as many cells as I am."

"Show-off," whispered Zoe.

"Why have you got more cells than us, sir?" asked Liam O'Brady.

"Because you're all still growing," said Mr Blood. "Even as I speak, your body cells are multiplying like crazy and adding more and more tissue to your body. Thrilling, isn't it?"

5-year-old Brian + lots of new cells = 7-year-old Brian

7-year-old Brian + lots of new cells = even bigger 10-year-old Brian

Liam suddenly picked up a ruler and started measuring his arms.

"Not quite *that* rapidly, Liam!" said Mr Blood.

"Er, Mr Blood?" said Simon. "If all this cell dividing is just going on and on and on, why don't human beings end up the size of skyscrapers?"

"Ha, good point Simon!" said Mr Blood. "Well, this rapid addition of cell tissue does end when you stop growing in your late teens."

He twiddled a few more dials on the X-magnascope, then stood back and said, "Have a look at this video simulation of *future-you*."

"That doesn't mean that all cell multiplication stops. Our cells are constantly wearing out and dying, so they need replacing. For example, our skin cells, which you already know about. The only cells that don't die are our brain cells. They have to last us our entire lifetime."

"Or, in Charlotte's case, until next Tuesday afternoon," said Brian from behind his screen.

"Will my brain keep growing until I'm nineteen?" I asked.

"Unfortunately not, Laxmi," laughed Mr Blood. "Your brain stops growing when you're about six. Brain experts believe that we're all born with the same amount of brain cells. These brain cells don't divide and multiply like other cells do. Instead, it's thought that the number of connections between our brain cells increase and become more complex as we grow up.

"If you imagine more and more telephone and internet links being set up between all the houses in the world so that more and more information can be sent, shared, processed and stored, you'll perhaps be able to understand what I mean."

"But we'll only be able to do that if we've got enough links between our brain cells!" said Daniel. "Ha ha!"

"My brain hurts just thinking about all this," said Brian.

"But how do you actually get brainier then?" said Charlotte.

"Stimulation," said Mr Blood. "In just the same way as exercising your muscles makes them more muscular, thinking makes your brain more brainy and probably increases your ability to think! It's said that babies who are talked to a lot and given tons of attention by their parents end up with brains that are 25% 'bigger' than babies who are neglected. But of course, by bigger I don't mean they've actually got more brain cells."

"So how many brain cells do we have altogether?" asked Zoe.

THERE ARE ABOUT A HUNDRED BILLION BRAIN CELLS UP THERE!

"Along with about a thousand billion other sorts of cells giving them back-up," Mr Blood continued.

"Cripes!" said Simon. "That sounds like a huge amount of cells!"

"It is," said Mr Blood. "Us humans are the brain-cell champions of the world. We've three times as many as a gorilla and seven million times as many as a stick insect."

"What, even Liam?" said Daniel.

"Yes, even Liam!" laughed Mr Blood. "Right, now I want to tell you a bit more about how we're actually put together."

He grinned slyly, showing his pointy teeth and said, "Kelly, would you get me a new board marker, please."

"No prob, Mr Blood!" said Kelly, and she nipped into the art store.

A moment later she let out a blood-curdling scream…

Brenda, Bob and Peter

Kelly ran out of the store looking whiter than the marker she was clutching. "There's *skellingtons* in there!" she screamed.

A second later we heard a creaking, clattering sound and we all turned white too because two full-sized skeletons came dancing out of the store clacking their teeth and grinning from ear to ear (except they didn't have any).

When we'd all finally stopped screaming, the smaller skeleton went and stood in front of Kelly and said, "No need to be scared of a skelly, Kelly! Bones is the name … Brenda Bones. And this is my husband, Bob. By the way dear, it's *skeletons*, not skellingtons."

"That's right," said the other skeleton. "And we're here to tell you children all about … guess what!"

"B-B-Bones?" stuttered Liam.

"Yes!" said Bob. "And lots more besides. We're made of 206 bones, same as most adult humans."

"However," said Brenda, "when you were all babies you had about 350 bones."

"How come?" said Daniel. "Do you lose them when you're growing up?"

"Course not!" said Bob. "They join together!"

"Your bones help you stay in shape!" said Brenda.

She put one of her bony hands on Daniel's head and said, "Imagine a frame tent without all its poles and struts. What would it do?"

"Er … just flop, I suppose?" said Daniel.

"Exactly!" said Brenda. "Same as you'd do if someone took away your bones."

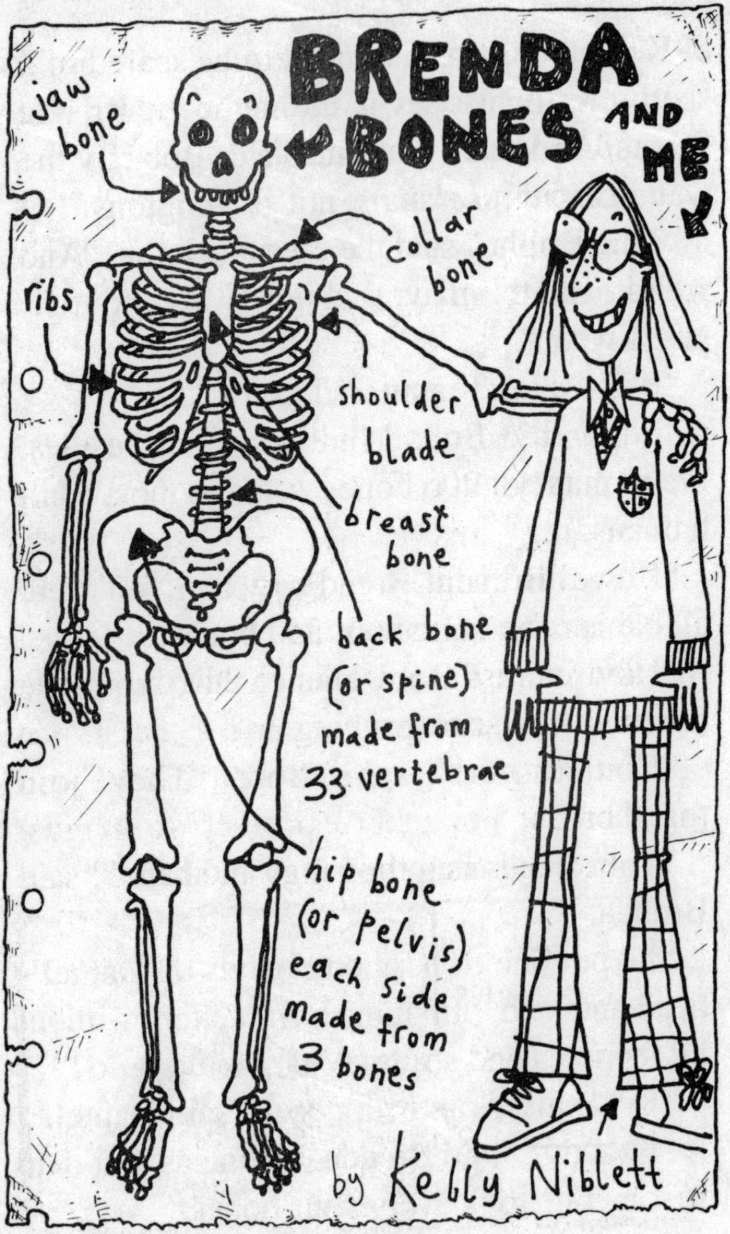

BRENDA BONES AND ME

jaw bone

collar bone

ribs

shoulder blade

breast bone

back bone (or spine) made from 33 vertebrae

hip bone (or pelvis) each side made from 3 bones

by Kelly Niblett

"Your bones are very strong," said Bob. "Stronger than steel. But they're light!" He pointed to Simon and said, "Pick me up!"

Simon put his arms around Bob's waist. And he lifted him up. Just like that!

"Your skeleton is strong and light and it protects your soft and squidgy inside bits," said Brenda.

She ran her finger bones backwards and forwards across Bob's ribs so that they made a sound like someone running a stick down some railings, saying, "Your rib cage and your breast bone here protect your most important organs – the lungs and heart."

WHILE YOUR 22 SKULL BONES PROTECT YOUR BRAIN!

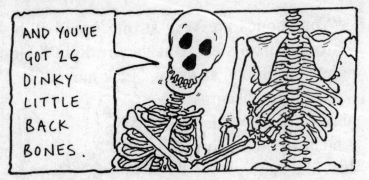

"They protect your delicate spinal cord," explained Brenda, "which contains the nerves that carry the messages whizzing between your brain and body."

"To protect us and give us shape," said Bob, "our bones need to be joined."

"But our skeletons also give us the ability to move," said Brenda.

"So for that," said Bob, "we need joints that can move too!"

WAYS OUR BONES ARE JOINED
by Laxmi

If it wasn't for our joints we'd all move stiffly — worse than robots!

walking without joints

There are three types of joints:

Hinged Joints

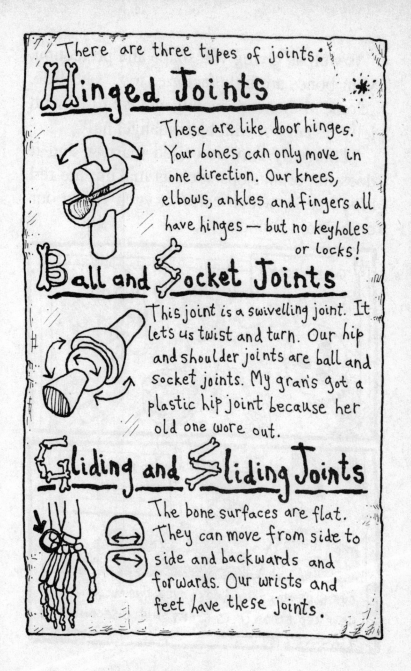

These are like door hinges. Your bones can only move in one direction. Our knees, elbows, ankles and fingers all have hinges — but no keyholes or locks!

Ball and Socket Joints

This joint is a swivelling joint. It lets us twist and turn. Our hip and shoulder joints are ball and socket joints. My gran's got a plastic hip joint because her old one wore out.

Gliding and Sliding Joints

The bone surfaces are flat. They can move from side to side and backwards and forwards. Our wrists and feet have these joints.

"As well as giving you shape and protection, your bones are little factories too," said Bob. "Some of them are spongy and are filled with jelly ... but not with blancmange, ha!"

"This jelly stuff is called marrow and it does important jobs such as making the red blood cells, which carry oxygen round our body," said Brenda.

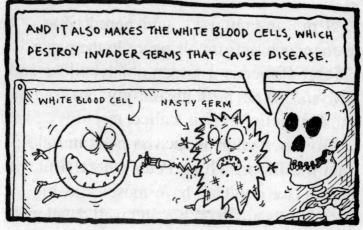

WHITE BLOOD CELL   NASTY GERM

AND IT ALSO MAKES THE WHITE BLOOD CELLS, WHICH DESTROY INVADER GERMS THAT CAUSE DISEASE.

"Excuse me," said Charlotte. "How do our bones move?"

"They certainly don't move all on their own," said Bob. Then he grinned and looked at Mr Blood, saying, "Well, not normally, they don't. This morning was an exception."

"I think it's time we brought in our next guest," said Mr Blood. He looked at our classroom door and said, "Come in, Peter."

The door swung open and a huge muscular man wearing nothing but a red leotard and golden trainers bounded into our classroom. He did three backflips, two somersaults and then a cartwheel.

"Wow, it's Peter Power!" I gasped. "At least I *think* it's him?"

35

"I'm sure it is!" whispered Zoe. "I recognize him from his photo in the paper."

Peter Power is a famous bodybuilder and TV star. And he's absolutely *covered* in muscles!

"To move your bones you need muscles," said Mr Blood. "Like Peter's here! But, of course, we don't all have muscles as big as Peter's. His are extra big and well developed because he works out at the gym every day."

"S'right, Mr Blood!" said Peter. "Now, can I offer you a *lift*?"

He suddenly grabbed Mr Blood and lifted him high above his head.

WE'VE ALL GOT MORE THAN 600 MUSCLES ATTACHED TO OUR SKELETONS. IN FACT 40% OF OUR ENTIRE BODY IS MADE OF MUSCLE.

BUT THEY'RE NOT ALL ATTACHED TO OUR SKELETONS.

"So do your biceps *pull* your arms and your triceps *push* them?" said Daniel

"No," said Peter. "They both *pull*!"

"No muscle in your body can push!" added Mr Blood. "All movement is done by teamwork between your various pairs of muscles. Look." And he pointed towards the window.

"But how do they do the pulling?" said Charlotte.

"It's your muscle cells," said Mr Blood. "Remember how I told you different cells did different jobs? Each of your muscle cells has got the special ability to shrink itself. So when they all shrink together the muscle *contracts*!"

40

"Excuse me, Peter," said Brian. "What's our biggest muscle?"

"You're sitting on it," said Peter. "It's called your *gluteus maximus*."

"He means your bottom!" said Mr Blood. "That's the Latin name. All our muscles have been given Latin names so that doctors all around the world know they're talking about the same thing. For instance, our stomach muscles are called the *rectus abdominus*."

"But I prefer to think of them as my six-pack," laughed Peter and then he began rippling his amazing stomach muscles.

And with that the muscle man and the skellies danced across our classroom and out of the door.

MY MUSCLES AND THEIR LATIN NAMES

by Liam O'Brady

that's me!

My sternocleidomastoid— I turn my head or move it forward with this muscle

My Pectoralis major— I use this to pull my arm forward and towards my body

My deltoids—I lift my shoulders with these
—shrug shrug!

My trapezius—I use this to keep my shoulders straight

My gracilis — I use this to bend and twist my leg

My tibialis anteriors — I lift my feet with these when I'm walking

My gluteus maximus — I sit on this one!

My sartorius — this one bends my leg

From gum to tum

"Our bodies need plenty of fuel for us to move all those marvellous muscles of ours," said Mr Blood. "In fact we need fuel just to go on living. We need it for energy, for growth and to repair ourselves. And the way we get that fuel is by…"

"Popping down the petrol station and filling up with premium unleaded!" said Daniel Mapson, quick as a flash.

"Yes, very funny!" said Mr Blood, when we'd all stopped laughing. "But as everyone except Daniel seems to know, we *don't* do that. To get our fuel we *eat*! We need food to stay alive. However, in order to release all the goodies from our food we must first break it down into tiny fragments called molecules. These food molecules are then taken into our blood, which transports them to our hungry body cells. And that whole job is called digestion."

He grinned, then reached into the top drawer of his desk, took out a huge sandwich and said, "I've got this delicious chicken tikka and salad sarnie with triple garlic mayonnaise to give away to any hungry person who is willing to help me in my next demonstration."

About half of the class began waving their arms to be picked. In the end Mr Blood chose Simon Sidworth.

"Now, Simon," said Mr Blood, "I want you to eat the sandwich. But before that I want everyone else to put on a pair of *these*!"

He opened a big box next to his desk and began taking out pairs of glasses.

They were about twice the size of ordinary glasses and their lenses were a strange, pinkish-green colour.

"What are they?" said Charlotte.

"TELESCOPE-ENABLED X-RAY SUPER-SPEX WITH A HOLOGRAMATIC LABELLING DEVICE!"

"The thing is," said Mr Blood, "the entire digestion process takes between 24 and 46 hours. These spex will enable us to see Simon's insides doing their stuff with fast-forward action or slow-motion replays at a tweak of my handset. They'll also guide you with hologramatic labels on his organs, give us close-ups *and* allow us to hear all the grunts, squeaks and rumbles! Don't worry, Simon, you won't miss a thing. I'm videoing it all!"

"Wow!" we all gasped.

While we were sorting out the super-spex, Simon sniffed the sandwich.

"He's checking it out with that sharp nose of his," said Mr Blood. "Which is a good way of testing its freshness. Bad smell: don't touch! Good smell: probably OK. So get stuck in! Maybe one of you lot ought to nose out a few fascinating nose facts sometime."

fried potatoes
baked beans
grilled mushrooms
sizzling bacon
toast

Nose: can recognize 10,000 different smells

The tongue only knows four tastes. You really need a nose to taste things properly! That's why things don't taste so good when you've got a cold. Thick mucus clogs up your smell receptors:

Delicious!

Is it?

Well done, Laxmi. By the way, did you know that in the old days doctors sniffed their patients to find out what diseases they had! Mr Blood

"OK! Glasses on!" said Mr Blood. "And eat away, Simon!"

We put on our super-spex and soon we were watching Simon eat and digest his sandwich, inside-out, in-depth and close-up!

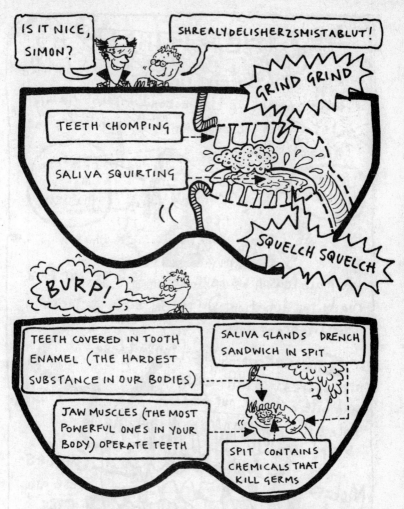

"Simon's three saliva glands squirt out two litres of fresh spit every single day of his life," said Mr Blood.

"Wow! Almost a bucketful!" gasped Daniel. "What a *gobsmacking* statistic!"

TEETH and CHEWING

by Charlotte

Tooth enamel is the second hardest natural substance in the whole world. Diamonds are the hardest.

Like my sparklers?

I prefer my gnashers!

The main reason we have teeth is to get our food ready for digestion. Different sorts of teeth do different jobs.

Incisors — at the front. These are shaped like little chisels and bite and slice our food... unless it's soup!

← hairy nose!

Canines — these are more pointy and they tear our food.

Molars and Premolars — these are broader and shovel-shaped. They crush, grind and chew our food.

And then it's all ready to swallow!

"Simon's nose, tongue and saliva are doing their bit to make sure he gets maximum taste enjoyment from the sarnie!" said Mr Blood. "And look! There it goes! Down the hatch! It's a swallow!"

UVULA: STOPS FOOD GOING UP HIS NOSE

CHEWED-UP SANDWICH BALL

SIMON'S TONGUE WORKS BALL TO BACK OF THROAT

EPIGLOTTIS: FLAP THAT FLIPS OVER SIMON'S WINDPIPE AND STOPS FOOD GOING DOWN THERE (SO HE DOESN'T CHOKE)

THROAT MUSCLES MOVING THE BALL OF FOOD TOWARDS HIS GULLET

Our Tongue by Zoe

We use our tongue:

to taste — *Yum yum*

to speak — *Yammer Yammer*

to push food into our mouths — *gulp gulp*

Taste signals go from taste buds on our tongue along nerve threads to our brain. If things taste horrible, you spit them out.

This is good because yukky-tasting stuff is often poisonous.

Different bits of the tongue recognize different tastes.

BITTER

SOUR

SWEET

SALTY

"Now," said Mr Blood. "The muscles of Simon's gullet are pushing the food ball towards his tum. It's a bit like squeezing a tennis ball along a wet vacuum cleaner tube."

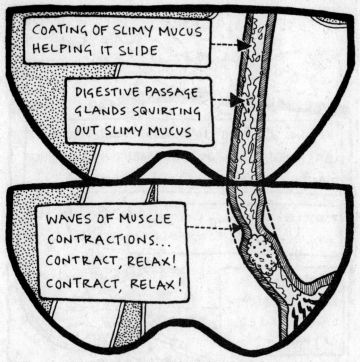

COATING OF SLIMY MUCUS HELPING IT SLIDE

DIGESTIVE PASSAGE GLANDS SQUIRTING OUT SLIMY MUCUS

WAVES OF MUSCLE CONTRACTIONS... CONTRACT, RELAX! CONTRACT, RELAX!

"Goooal!" cried Mr Blood. "Look, everyone. The ball's just landed in the net! I mean … it's landed in *Simon's tum*!"

"Cripes – that was fast!" said Kelly.

"Ten seconds, actually," said Daniel. "I counted."

"Well done!" said Mr Blood. "That is the time your food takes to travel from gum to tum. But it's in your tum rather longer than that – usually about three hours. So in a minute we'll speed things up a bit."

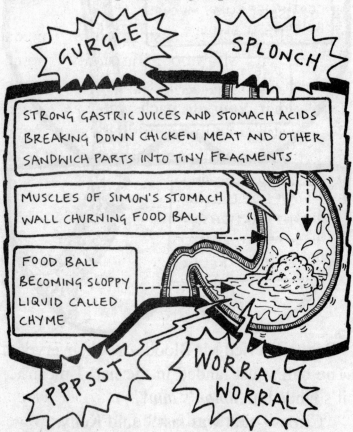

"That acid in Simon's tum is strong enough to burn your hand!" said Mr Blood.

Simon suddenly looked worried and quickly stopped chewing.

"Excuse me, Mr Blood," he said. "If these gastric juices are as strong as you say they are, isn't my stomach likely to end up, well, *eating* itself!"

"Excellent question, stomach … I mean *Simon*!" said Mr Blood, frantically tapping his teeth. "But your body's geared up for that. To avoid it, your stomach wall has a good thick coating of slime, a bit like the stuff you find up your nostrils. And that protects it from the strong gastric juices."

PHEW, THAT'S A RELIEF!

"We'll fast-forward now," said Mr Blood. "And we'll check out Simon's small intestine. This digestive tube of his is very narrow but it's really long; between five and eight metres."

"Look," said Mr Blood. The nutrients are now being absorbed into Simon's blood through thousands of tiny tubes called *villi*."

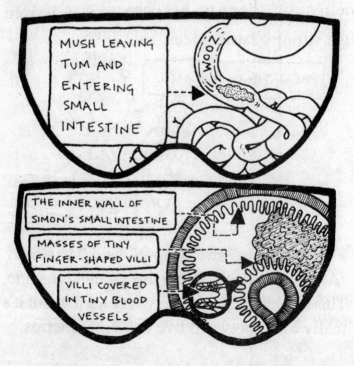

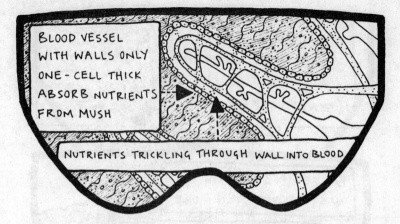

BLOOD VESSEL WITH WALLS ONLY ONE-CELL THICK ABSORB NUTRIENTS FROM MUSH

NUTRIENTS TRICKLING THROUGH WALL INTO BLOOD

"And now that's sorted, the blood will carry these nutrients around Simon's body, delivering them to his various cells. For instance, those energy-hungry muscle cells," said Mr Blood. "However, before they do, they'll run them past the liver, which will check them out for any nasties that may cause problems elsewhere in his body. If Simon's liver does come across any nasties, it'll identify them and pull them out of the blood. But we'll be learning more about the liver a bit later. Right! Now that the important nutrients have been extracted from the sarnie, all that's left is to dump the mainly useless waste leftovers. And that's the job of Simon's large intestine, his rectum and his anus."

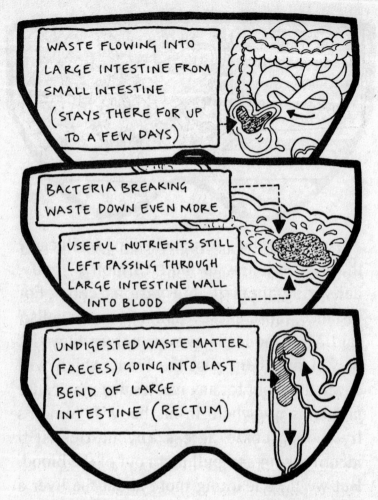

WASTE FLOWING INTO LARGE INTESTINE FROM SMALL INTESTINE (STAYS THERE FOR UP TO A FEW DAYS)

BACTERIA BREAKING WASTE DOWN EVEN MORE

USEFUL NUTRIENTS STILL LEFT PASSING THROUGH LARGE INTESTINE WALL INTO BLOOD

UNDIGESTED WASTE MATTER (FAECES) GOING INTO LAST BEND OF LARGE INTESTINE (RECTUM)

"And that's that!" said Mr Blood. "The sandwich is digested! Now, whenever it's convenient for him, Simon will nip to the loo and get rid of that undigested waste matter from his body."

"Can I ask a question?" said Daniel, still giggling. "Er … what causes, er … *farts*?"

"Well," said Mr Blood. "The whole digestion process produces waste gas, which we have to get rid of from one end or the other. Probably about 13 times each day."

"Right, I'm going to count mine from now on," said Daniel.

"Er, excuse me, Mr Blood?" said Brian. "If we eat lots of different-coloured things like yellow bananas, red peppers, blue sweets and green vegetables, why is our poo brown?"

"Two main reasons," said Mr Blood. "One is that if you mix up lots of colours they tend to end up a sludgy brown colour. The other is that dead red blood cells give the main colour to our faeces. And you lose an awful lot of *them* every day!"

"Uuuuurgh!" said the whole class.

"Time for lunch, everyone!" said Mr Blood cheerfully.

The personal organ-izer

When Mr Blood came into the classroom the next morning he was carrying something that looked like a widescreen telly under his arm.

"Good morning, children," said Mr Blood. "I thought I'd demonstrate my personal *organ*-izer today."

"My mum's got one of those but hers fits in her pocket!" I whispered to Zoe.

Mr Blood must have heard, because he laughed and said, "My *organ*-izer is a little different. Here's my first guest body *organ*!"

He opened the *organ*-izer so we could see its screens. The screen on the right was blank but on the left one was this big pink thing. And it was trembling slightly.

"Uurgh!" said Kelly. "What's *that*, Mr Blood?"

"It's a human liver, Kelly!" said Mr Blood. "Actual size, too!"

"Big, isn't it?" said Daniel.

"Ooer," said Charlotte. "Fancy that huge thing being inside a person!"

"The liver is the biggest and heaviest of all our organs," said Mr Blood. "But, then again, it needs to be. Altogether, it's got about 500 different jobs to do, many of which are to do with blood."

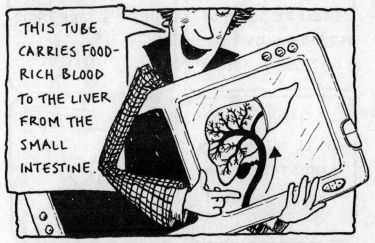

THIS TUBE CARRIES FOOD-RICH BLOOD TO THE LIVER FROM THE SMALL INTESTINE.

"Where the *villi* absorb the nutrients into the blood," I said, blushing.

"Well remembered, Laxmi!" said Mr Blood. "One of the liver's main jobs is adjusting the food content of the blood before it's taken off around the body to be served up to the waiting cells. Almost like a top chef getting the ingredients in the soup just right before it's served to the customers."

As Mr Blood spoke, the liver began to change and a moment later we all gasped then laughed as it turned into a little cartoon man in a white hat and stripy apron!

"I ALSO MAKE SURE ZE BLOOD IS NICE AND CLEAN BY FILTERING OUT NASTY POISONS AND DEAD RED BLOOD CELLS SO THEY CAN BE THROWN AWAY."

"UUURGH! WE DON'T WANT ZEM IN ZERE!"

Mr Blood clicked a switch on the *organ*-izer and the screens went blank.

"And once your blood's clean, off it goes to your cells loaded with nutrients and oxygen," he said.

"Which means they can create energy!" said Brian.

"Exactly!" said Mr Blood. "OK … time for the next celebrity organs."

He flicked the switch and these two objects appeared on the *organ*-izer.

"Two kidney-bean-shaped things," said Charlotte.

"Which are?" said Mr Blood.

"Two kidney beans, of course!" said Daniel.

"Don't be daft, Daniel," said Mr Blood. "Of course, they're not. They're kidneys!"

"That's a coincidence, then," said Zoe. "That they're kidney-bean-shaped and called kidneys as well!"

"The beans were named after the organs," said Mr Blood. "Not the other way round."

"What do they do?" asked Brian.

"I'll let them tell you," said Mr Blood.

As he spoke the kidneys began to morph, just like the liver had done, and the next moment they'd been replaced by these two cartoon characters.

"US KIDNEYS ARE YOUR BODY'S CLEAN-UP SQUAD."

"YES! WE'RE THE CLEAN-UP KIDS! WELL, CLEAN-UP KIDNEYS ACTUALLY."

"OUR JOB IS TO SORT OUT ALL THE WASTE LEFTOVERS THAT DON'T GO INTO YOUR LARGE INTESTINE AND DOWN TO YOUR RECTUM!"

"THAT'S MAINLY THE CHEMICAL LEFTOVERS FROM THE DIFFERENT PROCESSES TAKING PLACE ROUND YOUR BODY."

"AND YOUR WASTE TOO."

"WE ACT LIKE A COUPLE OF SIEVES."

"WE CLEAN AND FILTER ALL THE BLOOD IN YOUR BODY OVER AND OVER AGAIN."

Mr Blood flicked his *organ*-izer switch and the Clean-up Kids were instantly replaced by the kidney picture again.

"They're the ureters," said Mr Blood. "The mixture of waste chemicals and water drips down them. It's called urine and it eventually ends up in the bladder."

"Aah!" said Liam, giggling. "I know about urine and bladders. You're talking about going to the toilet, aren't you?"

"We are," said Mr Blood. "So let's have a look at a bladder now."

He clicked again and this appeared on the *organ*-izer:

"It's a stretchy muscular bag," explained Mr Blood, "that expands as it fills up with the waste chemicals and water."

"It's looking quite full already, if you ask me," said Daniel.

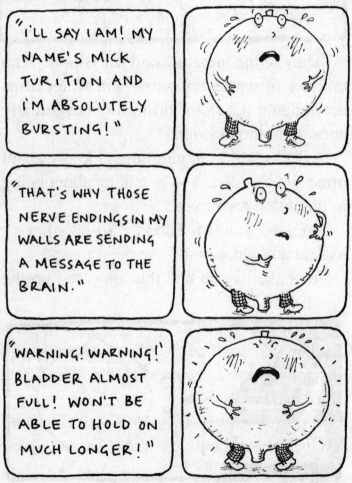

"I'LL SAY I AM! MY NAME'S MICK TURITION AND I'M ABSOLUTELY BURSTING!"

"THAT'S WHY THOSE NERVE ENDINGS IN MY WALLS ARE SENDING A MESSAGE TO THE BRAIN."

"WARNING! WARNING! BLADDER ALMOST FULL! WON'T BE ABLE TO HOLD ON MUCH LONGER!"

"Sensors let your brain know when you need a wee," said Mr Blood. "So then you go to the loo, where you relax a little muscle known as a sphincter and have a tiddle."

"Oh dear," said Mr Blood and quickly flicked the *organ*-izer switch again. In an instant both the bladder *and* the puddle on the floor had vanished.

"Er, excuse me, Mr Blood," said Charlotte. "Why does my baby brother have to wear a nappy all the time?"

"Well," said Mr Blood. "Every time a baby's bladder gets full it empties immediately because the baby's brain hasn't developed sufficiently for it to learn to control its sphincter muscle."

"That's what you call potty-training, then?" I said.

"That's right, Laxmi," said Mr Blood. "Now, I think we're all ready for a *breath of fresh air*. But before we go outside for that we'll take a quick look at these!"

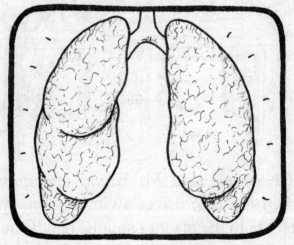

"I know what they are," I said. "They're lungs, aren't they Mr Blood?"

Before he had time to reply … the lungs had morphed!

"THAT'S RIGHT, WE ARE LUNGS!"
"WE'RE HUFFY AND PUFFY... THE WINDBAG TWINS."

"AS YOU ALL KNOW, YOU NEED OXYGEN TO SURVIVE." "BUT YOU CAN'T STORE IT LIKE YOU DO THINGS LIKE FATS AND SUGARS."

"SO OUR JOB IS TO KEEP YOU SUPPLIED WITH IT..."
"...24 HOURS A DAY, 7 DAYS A WEEK."

"YOU TAKE ABOUT 25,000 BREATHS EVERY DAY."
"AND EVERY TIME YOU DO YOU GET VITAL OXYGEN FROM EACH GULP OF AIR YOU TAKE IN."

25,000 BREATHS

"YOU BREATHE IN AND THE AIR GOES INTO YOUR WINDPIPE..."
"NEXT IT FLOWS THROUGH YOUR TWO BRONCHI..."

"THEN YOUR BRONCHIOLES..."
"THEN THE AIR SACS CALLED ALVEOLI."

"OXYGEN FROM AIR PASSES THROUGH THE REALLY THIN WALLS OF THE ALVEOLI INTO THE BLOOD CAPILLARIES THAT SURROUND THEM."

"SO THAT'S IT... THE OXYGEN'S IN YOUR BLOODSTREAM!"

"That's a bit like the nutrients going into the bloodstream from the *villi*," said Brian.

"A very similar system," said Mr Blood.

"BUT THAT'S NOT ALL WE DO!" "THE NUTRIENTS AND OXYGEN IN YOUR CELLS PRODUCE ENERGY."

"AND ALSO A WASTE GAS CALLED CARBON DIOXIDE." "THIS PASSES OUT THROUGH YOUR CAPILLARY WALLS INTO YOUR ALVEOLI."

CARBON DIOXIDE

"THEN BACK UP YOUR WINDPIPE AND OUT THROUGH YOUR MOUTH AND NOSE." "IT'S ALL BEAUTIFULLY WORKED OUT!"

"But that's by no means the end of the story," said Mr Blood as he finally closed up his amazing *organ*-izer. "There's a really important purpose behind the loading of our blood with fresh oxygen. We…"

"…don't just do it for the sake of our health!" chipped in Daniel.

Then he went bright red as Mr Blood said, "Well that's where you're wrong, Daniel. That's *exactly* what we do it for! We'll be finding out what happens to that oxygen-rich blood next. But now I must scoot. I've got a very important football game to referee!"

Mr Blood pulled out his whistle and gave it a cheerful blow, then he disappeared out of the door.

Lub-dup, lub-dup, lub-dup

After break on Wednesday we were waiting for Mr Blood to return from the staffroom when a vampire leapt into the centre of the room, flapping its cape and snarling.

I AM COUNT GORE-BLIMEY AND FRESH BLOOD REALLY IS MY CUP OF TEA!

Then, just as we were all about to run screaming from the room, the vampire removed its mask and said, "Only me! Just joking!" and we saw it was Mr Blood!

"Oh, Mr Blood," I said. "You terrified us. My heart's thumping like mad."

"So's mine," said everyone else. "You really frightened us, Mr Blood."

"And do you know why your hearts are all pounding so violently?" said Mr Blood as he gave us an extra-long glimpse of those very weird teeth of his.

"Because we were scared, of course!" said Daniel.

"No, it's *far* more interesting than that," said Mr Blood. "You see, if I *had* been after your blood you would have needed to run away. Or perhaps even to fight me. And for that you'd require lots of extra energy in the form of oxygen and food. So your hearts are now working twice as hard pumping blood round your body – so that extra oxygen and food get to your muscle cells and brain cells as quickly as possible to deal with this emergency that turned out not to be an emergency."

"My heart feels like it will carry on thumping for ever," I said.

"It'll settle down to its normal rate soon,

Laxmi," said Mr Blood. "Which is somewhere around 90 beats per minute because you're a youngster. But my adult heart beats at somewhere between 60 and 70 times a minute and a baby's heart beats at 140 times a minute."

"So why is it faster when you're younger?" said Brian.

"Because the younger you are, the more growing you've got to do. So your blood has to do more rushing around to deliver all that vital food and energy and stuff. It's like a really busy building site with lorries constantly arriving with new building materials and workers going flat out to get the job finished on time."

"I listened to my heart through our doctor's stethoscope once," said Daniel. "It made a sort of *lub-dup, lub-dup, lub-dup* sound."

"That's what we call our heartbeat!" said Mr Blood.

"What actually is a heartbeat? said Simon.

"You'll find out in two ticks!" said Mr Blood. He snapped his fingers and our whiteboard disappeared to reveal a huge hole in the classroom wall. *This* was behind it!"

We all stared in amazement at the reddish-brown lump with all its weird-looking tubes.

"A normal-sized heart is actually only about the size of a human fist," said Mr Blood. "Nevertheless, it's one of our most vital and hard-working organs. It thumps away 24 hours a day, 7 days a week, 52 weeks a year,

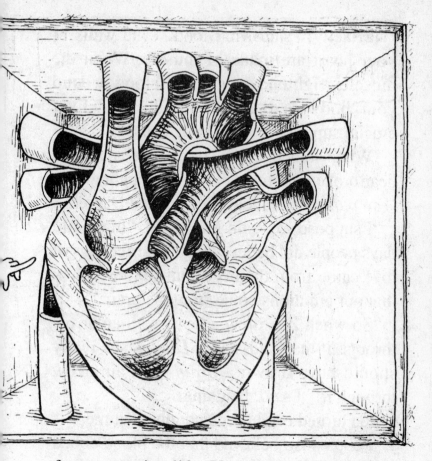

for our entire life. Your heart beats about 100,000 times a day – that's assuming you don't spend your time running away from tigers or wrestling crocodiles! So altogether it will beat about three billion times during your whole life. And when it stops, we stop…"

"Dead!" said Zoe. (She's always *so* cheerful!)

"Exactly!" said Mr Blood. "The walls of your heart are made of muscle. When the muscles tighten, they pump blood around your body so that the blood can deliver crucial supplies to your body cells."

"When someone in a soppy film says, 'I'm heartbroken, darling,' they really ought to say, 'I'm *pump*broken, darling!'" joked Daniel.

"I suppose so," said Mr Blood. "In the old days people did believe that all our feelings of love came from the heart, but we now know that our emotions come from the brain."

"So when Zoe drew a heart with an arrow through it that said, *I love Daniel*, she really should have drawn a *brain* with an arrow through it!" I said, laughing.

Zoe turned bright red and glared at me.

"People also believed that the blood ebbed and flowed from the heart, just as the tide at the seaside washes in and out," said Mr Blood. "Then, around 1628, a man called William Harvey discovered that our 4.5 litres of blood keeps flowing around and around our body in a non-stop mission to keep all the different body parts supplied with all the stuff we need for survival. And it's this lump of muscle and tubes you see before you that keeps the non-stop *circulation* going."

"It's not very heart-shaped is it?" said Zoe, looking at the huge heart.

"It's *perfectly* heart-shaped," said Mr Blood. "It's the cartoon versions that are wrong."

"What are those compartments for?" asked Simon.

"Your heart has four separate rooms, or *atriums* as they're properly known," said Mr Blood.

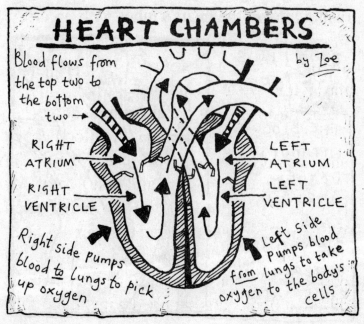

HEART CHAMBERS

by Zoe

Blood flows from the top two to the bottom two →

RIGHT ATRIUM

LEFT ATRIUM

RIGHT VENTRICLE

LEFT VENTRICLE

Right side pumps blood to lungs to pick up oxygen

Left side pumps blood from lungs to take oxygen to the body's cells

"Now, just to make sure we don't miss a thing when this heart starts beating, I've set all the action in slow motion. Is everyone ready to see this huge heart throb?!"

"What huge heartthrob?" said Charlotte. "Is a pop star coming to see us?"

"He means, see that big heart up there beat!" said Zoe. "I'm definitely ready."

"Yeah, we are too!" everyone yelled.

"Let's hope I can get it working," said Mr Blood. Then he clicked his fingers and we heard a great gushing sound and liquid began rushing down the heart's tubes.

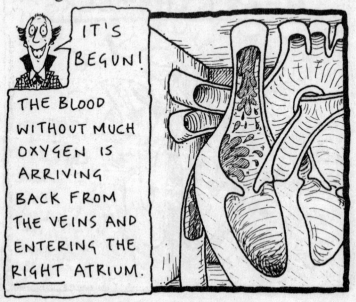

IT'S BEGUN!

THE BLOOD WITHOUT MUCH OXYGEN IS ARRIVING BACK FROM THE VEINS AND ENTERING THE RIGHT ATRIUM.

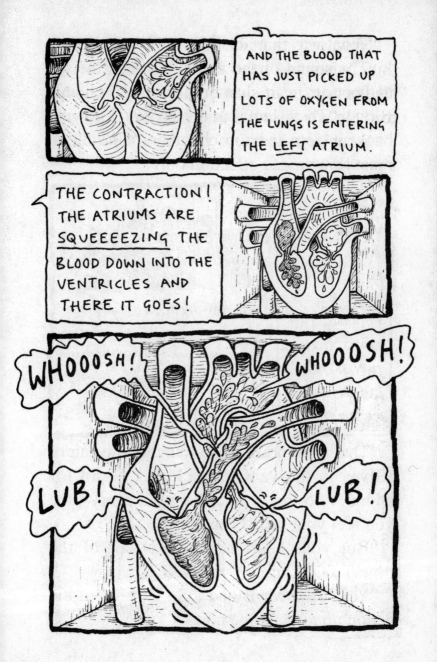

"What was that noise?" said Daniel.

"The sound of the valves between the top and bottom heart chambers shutting," said Mr Blood. "They slam shut to stop blood flowing back up into the top chambers. The blood must flow in one direction only!"

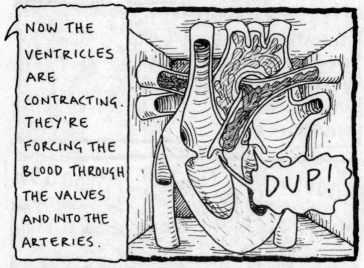

NOW THE VENTRICLES ARE CONTRACTING. THEY'RE FORCING THE BLOOD THROUGH THE VALVES AND INTO THE ARTERIES.

DUP!

"That DUP noise is the sound of the pair of valves in the ventricles closing," said Mr Blood. "So that's what happens every time you feel your heart 'beat'."

"But your heart beats loads, all of the time?" said Liam.

"Yes," said Mr Blood. "So let's speed the action up to real time now!"

The blood now began to flow through the chambers really quickly with the two sets of valves shutting one after the other on every count. It was deafening, too, like someone regularly beating a huge drum.

"Every time the heart lub-dups it pumps about two-thirds of a litre of blood," shouted Mr Blood. "In other words, it's pumping over five litres (or a gallon) of blood in just one minute."

"Wow, that is a lot!" said Simon. "Over 7,000 litres a day."

"And that adds up to an amazing total of 2,628,000 litres a year!" said Charlotte.

"Your maths is improving, Charlotte!" said Mr Blood. (He'd not spotted she was using her calculator.)

"Which would be about 184 million litres by the time you're 70!" said "Three Brains" (who was now using his calculator, too).

"All this *circulation* of your blood takes place in tubes known as blood vessels," said Mr Blood. "Altogether, each one of us has around 95,000 kilometres (60,000 miles) of them winding around our insides.

"*What*?" we all gasped.

"*Sixty thousand* miles of blood vessels," repeated Mr Blood. "They could wind twice round the world with enough left over to wrap around the Himalayas a few dozen times."

"Cool!" we all said.

"Look at your hands," said Mr Blood.

We all looked.

"Uuuurgh!" said Charlotte. "I've got blue worms in me wrists!"

"Those aren't worms," said Mr Blood. "They're blood vessels. I'll let you find out about them all for homework."

BLOOD VESSELS by Charlotte

Blood vessels are tubes ————▶
Your blood flows through them.
There are 3 sorts:

① ARTERIES! big strong blood vessels. They carry blood full of oxygen and food to your body cells. When they get near the parts that need oxygen and food they split into smaller branches. The branches split into even smaller capillaries.

A bit like motorways:

Oxygen Oxygen

←BRANCH
ARTERY

NUTRIENT
NUTRIENTS
NUTRIENTs
Oxygen Oxygen Oxygen
Oxygen NUTRIENTS Oxygen Oxygen NUTRIENTS

② CAPILLARIES: blood vessels too but they're really tiny and thin. Their walls are only one-cell thick. So nutrients and oxygen can easily pass through them into the cells of your body tissues.

NUT
O₂

③ VEINS: take blood loaded with waste products back to the heart. You can see your veins when you look at your wrist.

HEART

time to get loaded up!

WASTE

VEIN

"Right, let's talk about blood itself," said Mr Blood, and he stuck a pin in his finger. A moment later a tiny speck of blood appeared on his skin.

"Yuck!" cried Charlotte. "You're bleeding!" (She's not too keen on the sight of blood.)

DON'T WORRY. THERE'S PLENTY MORE WHERE THAT CAME FROM.

"As I said before, most adults have about 4.5 litres of blood pulsing around their circulatory system and you can actually lose 1.5 litres of that and survive. However, if you lose much more than 2 litres of it you're in big trouble!"

"Blood's blood," said Daniel staring at the red spot.

"Of course blood's blood, Daniel," said Kelly. "What else would it be? Orange squash?"

"No, Kelly, I mean it's Mr Blood's blood," said Daniel.

"In this single tiny drop here there are probably more than *two million* red blood cells, 5,000 white blood cells and 250,000 things called platelets," said Mr Blood. "And they're all slopping around in browny-yellow stuff called plasma. But in addition to that there are also tiny amounts of oxygen, food and waste matter. It's all worth looking into."

90

The Main Things in our Blood

by Zoe Thompson.

Red blood cells carry oxygen to every cell in your body tissues. Every single second, two million of your red blood cells are made and two million die.

White blood cells. Some white blood cells patrol around your blood looking for germs to attack. They live for about a week.

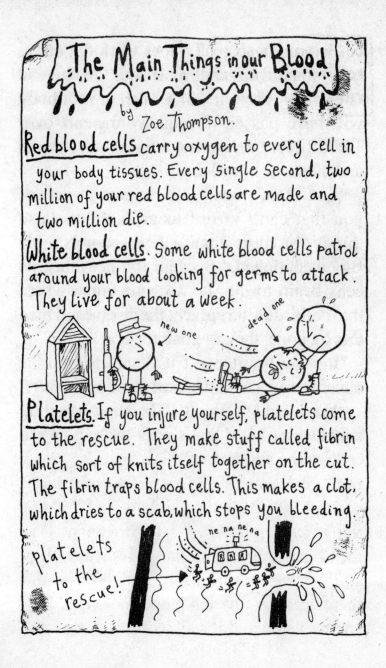

new one

dead one

Platelets. If you injure yourself, platelets come to the rescue. They make stuff called fibrin which sort of knits itself together on the cut. The fibrin traps blood cells. This makes a clot, which dries to a scab, which stops you bleeding.

platelets to the rescue!

ne na ne na

"So your heart really does work flat out to keep you alive," said Mr Blood. "At the end of each day every red blood cell in your body will have passed through your heart over 1,000 times, delivering life-giving oxygen and nutrients to cells."

"And there's one really important part of you that can't afford to go without those things for more than a few seconds," Mr Blood continued. "Because if it does then its cells begin to die. It's the one organ where the cells don't replace themselves. Once they're gone, they're gone for ever!"

"It's the brain, isn't it?" said Simon. "I remember you telling us that at the beginning."

"Yes," said Mr Blood. "The mind-boggling human brain. And that's what we're going to be learning about next."

Brainworld

"Good morning, children," said Mr Blood when he came into the classroom on Thursday. "Today, we're going to be exploring the most mysterious, most amazing and most puzzling body part of them all."

OH, SO WE'RE GOING TO BE TALKING ABOUT BELLY BUTTONS!

"No, Daniel, we're not," said Mr Blood. "Nor are we going to be talking about big toes! We're going to be exploring the human brain. The bit of you that really is the *real* you is also the mysterious body bit that scientists know least about!

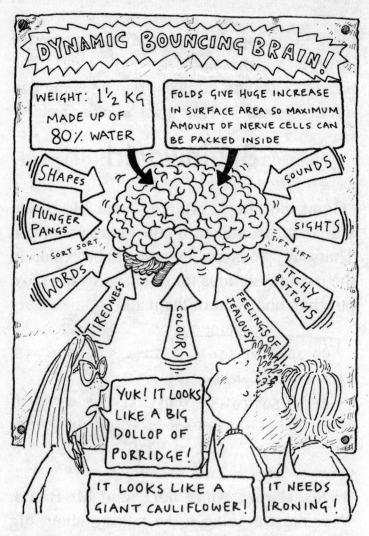

"Our brains are constantly trying to make some sort of sense of this huge and complicated world we live in," continued Mr Blood. "That wrinkled mass of grey jelly up there just happens to be the most powerful information processor on our planet. The brain of even the dimmest human being can outperform the world's most advanced super-computer."

"There you are, Brian," said Charlotte. "There's hope for you yet!"

"And thousands of questions about the brain remain unanswered," said Mr Blood. "For example, why some people are able to dream up phenomenal new inventions like electric toasters and CD players, while others have difficulty remembering their postcode."

"And why Liam always eats his peas with his spoon," said Daniel.

"And why Daniel Mapson has the sort of brain that forces him to make a joke every three minutes," went on Mr Blood.

We were still laughing when we heard a frightened cry from the far end of the room. It was Charlotte Edwards.

"Mr Blood!" she yelled. "There's a … a … a … huge nose growing out of the wall."

We all turned round and stared. In fact not only had a giant nose appeared by the art sink, but a great big *ear* was growing out of the wall too – and it was getting bigger every second!

"Excellent!" said Mr Blood. "Come on, everyone. What are we waiting for?"

By the time we got to the wall the ear had grown to the size of a small front door and before we knew it, Mr Blood was climbing inside it and saying, "Follow me!"

"Where are we, Mr Blood?" said Daniel, as we all clambered into the passageway.

"The canal," said Mr Blood.

"The canal?" said Daniel. "So are we going swimming then?"

"The *ear* canal!" said Mr Blood. "We're using it to reach the main brain area. Perhaps it's time you found out about ears, Daniel!"

"Ear! Ear!" said Charlotte.

How our ears work
by Daniel Mapson

Sound makes air ripples like throwing stones in a pond makes water ripples.

Now this happens:

① Air ripples go in my ear

② They make my ear drum skin vibrate

③ That makes other stuff vibrate

④ The vibrations reach little nerve cells which turn them into electrical signals

⑤ My brain turns the electrical signals into this...

to the brain

Daniel! Stop that!

98

When we finally reached the end of the ear tunnel we came to a big sign that said "Welcome to Brainworld". Underneath it was this guide to the brain's different departments.

TO THE **CEREBRUM**:
brain central – thinking, decision-making, smelling, tasting, touch, memory, storage, muscle control, understanding, language... and lots more!

TO THE **CEREBELLUM**:
balance checks, movement checks, muscle monitoring.

TO THE **BRAIN STEM**:
joins brain to spinal cord and rest of the body – carries signals to and from the brain.

TO THE **THALAMUS**:
the message sorter... decides which part of the brain to send different incoming information to.

TO THE **HYPOTHALAMUS**:
controls temperature, hunger, tiredness, heartbeat rate, sleeping, weeing... and more.

"We're inside a giant real-time working replica of a brain," said Mr Blood. "It matches a real brain's every action and thought. As the owner of this brain goes about their daily business, we'll be able to experience their brain handling incoming data, see what they're seeing, hear what they're thinking and feel what they're feeling!"

"Wow!" said Daniel.

"Spoooooky!" said Kelly.

"If you look over to the right you can see just in front of the brain are the eyes," said Mr Blood. "And these are the connections that bring all the sight information to the brain to be processed."

"Perhaps one of you would like to *see* what you can find out about seeing?" said Mr Blood.

EYES AND SEEING

by Laxmi

Light rays bounce off objects then come in through tiny holes in your eyes called pupils.

Not this sort...   ...but this sort.

schoolchild →

eye
pupil

The light rays go on to a screen thing at the back of your eye called the retina.

The picture ends up upside down on the retina – the retina changes it into electrical signals which go along your optic nerve to your brain which sees the picture and turns it the right way up.

"OK!" said Mr Blood. "We're going to spend a minute or so having a peep into the various bits of Brainworld, and then we'll all take a proper look inside the cerebrum."

CEREBRUM:
SEEING – What an ace skateboard!
THINKING – Wonder who left that lying around?
DECISION-MAKING – Think i'll have a quick whizz on it...
CEREBRUM:
MOVEMENT – WOW! What speed!
THINKING – Gonna do a back flip!
CEREBELLUM:
BALANCE – Oh cripes! I'm losing it!

THALAMUS: Sends message from skin sensors to cerebrum touch area: Incoming pain sensation
CEREBRUM: SENSATIONS - Ugh! Aaagh! Ouch!
THINKING - My ankle feels bust... and so's the skateboard!
THALAMUS: Sends message from optic nerve to seeing area: Incoming large-boy image.
CEREBRUM:
FEELINGS - Oh no! It's Smelly Darren.
MEMORY - Uh-Oh! Just remembered who the skateboard belongs to...
SMELLING - And he really is smelly!
CEREBRUM: THINKING - I'm in BIG trouble here...
HYPOTHALAMUS: Heart rate increasing. Temperature rising rapidly. Will need to empty bladder soon...
CENSORED

"OK!" said Mr Blood. "This is the cerebrum. It's the main chunk of our thinking tackle and makes up 90% of the brain. It picks up tons of incoming info from all our senses, makes sense of it all *and* enables us to think and decide on any action we take."

"But why does that sign point to the Left and Right and why is there that big groove down the centre?" I asked.

"Our cerebrums are divided into two halves called hemispheres," said Mr Blood. "They each have different tasks to perform. Step inside the right brain hemisphere and you'll see what I mean."

WELCOME TO THE
RIGHT CEREBRAL
HEMISPHERE

Jobs done here include: thinking in pictures, drawing, painting, being creative, enjoying music.

Some things the brain owner has done with their right cerebral hemisphere today:

1. Sketched a design for their perfect skateboard.

2. Pictured what the finished job would look like.

3. Sang along with their radio.

4. Imagined eating their lunch of fishfingers and chips.

"Now we'll cross the bridge into the left cerebral hemisphere," said Mr Blood.

Some things the brain owner has done with their left cerebral hemisphere today:

1. Worked out that it was probably best to put on their socks before their shoes (after a few false starts).

2. Worked out how many weeks' pocket money it would take to buy Smelly Darren a new skateboard.

3. Counted how much money they had in their piggy bank.

4. Thought what they'd say to Smelly.

WELCOME TO THE

LEFT CEREBRAL HEMISPHERE

Jobs done here include: figuring out problems, doing sums, speaking, writing, understanding science.

"Right!" said Mr Blood. "Time we were going. Just make your way along that passage, then squeeze through that little hole at the end there."

We did as he said and the next thing we knew, we were sliding down some sort of shoot. And a moment after that we all tumbled on to our classroom floor.

"Cripes!" I said. "Look, everyone. We've slid down the great big nose!"

"And all down the same nostril," laughed Mr Blood. "Well … at least it was a nice clean one!"

"Hey, Daniel's missing!" said Liam. "He must still be in there!"

The next second Daniel fell out of the nose's other nostril.

"Uuurgh!" he said, as he climbed to his feet. "I've got some sticky stuff on my trousers."

"You know what that is, don't you?" said Brian.

Daniel looked at his trousers a bit more closely and his face fell a mile.

"What's up, Daniel?" said Zoe. "You look like you've seen a *bogey* man."

"Don't tease him!" said Kelly "'*Snot* funny!"

Hairy Tongue Disease

When Mr Blood came in the next morning he plonked a large black doctor's bag on his desk and said, "Bad news. There's been a serious outbreak of AHTD."

He opened the bag and took out a ginormous hypodermic syringe. We all gasped.

"Wh-What's AHTD?" Daniel stammered.

"Anderson's Hairy Tongue Disease," said Mr Blood. "I will need to give you all an anti-AHTD jab."

Mr Blood squirted a little liquid out of the syringe, and everyone groaned.

"OK! Roll up your right sleeves!" said Mr Blood. "We'll do you first, Simon. Come here, please."

But Simon gripped the mat like he was glued to it.

Mr Blood burst out laughing and said, "I'm just winding you up."

"Phew!" said Daniel. "You really had us going there!"

"I know!" laughed Mr Blood. "Luckily, there's no such disease as Anderson's Hairy Tongue Disease! I made it up."

Putting down the syringe, Mr Blood continued, "However, there are some really *horrible* diseases around. All over the place there are thousands of microscopic nasties that can give us real diseases such as typhoid, rat-bite fever and cholera."

"You're talking about germs," said Kelly. "My dad's told me about them. He's forever wiping down our kitchen worktops to get rid of them."

"Why would your dad want to get rid of your kitchen worktops?" said Daniel.

"Ignore him, Kelly," said Mr Blood. "Yes, I am talking about germs. They include the notorious nasties known as bacteria and viruses."

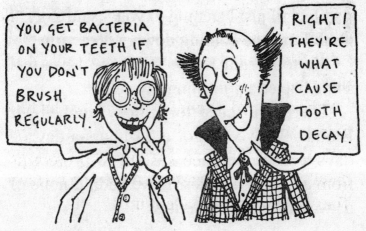

YOU GET BACTERIA ON YOUR TEETH IF YOU DON'T BRUSH REGULARLY.

RIGHT! THEY'RE WHAT CAUSE TOOTH DECAY.

"Bacteria are found everywhere," continued Mr Blood, "but not all of them are harmful. Those that are make poisonous waste chemicals which can cause things like throat infections and the lung disease tuberculosis."

"And what do viruses do?" said Brian.

"Viruses can't live on their own so they invade your body cells, then use them as little workshops where they make more viruses that eventually begin killing off the cells," said Mr Blood. "Colds and flu are caused by viruses. But they can also give you things like mumps and warts."

"Cripes, Mr Blood, there are *loads* of dangerous things out there!" said Daniel, looking alarmed again.

"I feel ill just listening to you!" said Zoe. "I think I may be coming down with a virus!"

"Me too," said Kelly. "I'm sure I can feel some bacteria poisoning my cells!"

"There's no need to panic!" laughed Mr Blood. "We've all got a 24-hours-a-day, 7-days-a-week defence system to protect us from all these baddies. If we hadn't, none of us would last five minutes."

Our Dynamic Defences against the Evil Invaders

~ by Kelly, Zae and Daniel ~

Our skin — we're wrapped in skin, which is a germ-proof barrier.

There's no way we can get in.

Unless we can find a hole, like a mouth or a nostril.

Or somewhere where the skin has been broken.

Eyelids and eyelashes and tears cover our eyes and wash them like little windscreen wipers — our tears carry anti-germ chemicals.

flick flick!
splat splat!

Nose hairs and mucus — all sticky so they trap germs going up our nostrils.

I'm all stuck up!

Ear wax (and loads of ear hair in old people) — sticky too, so it traps germs coming into our ears.

Me too!

Spit — chemicals in it kill the germs in food.

Look's like this spit's going to... aaaahh!

Stomach acid — kills other germs in food.

I got this far but now I'm being destroyed by... aaaagh!

Tonsils — Kill germs in our throat.

"LOVE GERMS"

GERM CARE

Tonsils out! Tonsils out!

White blood cells — zap the germs that get into our bodies.

Calling all white blood cells! Go to grazed kneecap!

Run for it! It's the terminator squad!

"Right! Hands up everyone who's had chicken pox!" said Mr Blood.

About nine people (including me) put up their hands.

"Now put your hand up if you've had chicken pox twice," said Mr Blood.

No one put up their hand.

"Just as I expected," said Mr Blood. "People hardly ever get chicken pox twice because the first time it strikes your white blood cells work out what sort of germs these intruders are, then they make chemicals called antibodies which destroy them. The first time the intruders come, the cells haven't got a very big supply of the right sort of antibodies."

WHICH IS WHY YOU GET THE CHICKEN POX!

SPOT ON, KELLY! HA HA!

"But the next time the invaders come, the white blood cells are all tooled up with huge stocks of the right sort of antibodies and they zap them in no time," explained Mr Blood.

"Which is why you don't get chicken pox twice!" I said, excitedly.

"That's it!" said Mr Blood. "Throughout your life your white blood cells are identifying different germs and making new antibodies to destroy them. By the time you're an adult your white blood cells will be able to identify about 100 million different germs and create the right antibodies to thwack every one of them!"

"Er, Mr Blood," said Simon. "What if a disease comes along that's so deadly that your white blood cells don't get a second chance to zap it because it's damaged you or even finished you off?"

"Good question!" said Mr Blood. Then, quite unexpectedly, he glanced at our whiteboard and said, "Oh look, no one's written up the date. I'll do it!"

"Mr Blood, you've got the date wrong," Charlotte called out.

"Oh no I haven't," said Mr Blood.

As Mr Blood spoke the whole classroom filled with thick mist.

After a moment the mist cleared and we saw we were no longer sitting on the mat but on a grass bank by a lane next to some thatched cottages. Quite nearby was a barn full of cows being milked by a row of girls sitting on wooden stools.

"This is the village of Berkeley in Gloucestershire," explained Mr Blood. "Sometime during the late 18th century. Exciting, isn't it?"

A boy and a man were leaning on a gate just next to us. The man was dressed in a long brown coat and had his hair in a sort of ponytail. The boy was wearing old-fashioned clothes and big muddy boots.

"Oh, there you are, Mr Blood!" said the man. "I'm so pleased you could make it."

CHILDREN, THIS IS DR EDWARD JENNER.

"He's got an interesting story to tell you," said Mr Blood. "I'll let him take over now."

"Thank you, Mr Blood," said Dr Jenner. "Well, children, I recently made a rather amazing discovery. And now I have high hopes that it will save my fellow human beings from smallpox. This wretched disease strikes mainly small children and young people, and kills one in every three of its victims. In fact I've had the dashed smallpox myself. It begins with a fever and headache and backache. It's all *most* distressing."

"But then things get worse!" said the boy. "A horrible rash breaks out all over your skin then that turns into dirty great pustules what go all crusty and dribbly. And if you do survive the smallpox, you get horrible scars from the pustules."

"And it can send you blind and deaf, too!" said Dr Jenner.

"He should know," said James. "He's the doctor round these parts."

"I am," said Dr Jenner. "And some time ago, during my rounds, I noticed that even though the smallpox rages so terribly throughout our green and pleasant land, the milkmaids round here never ever catch it."

He pointed to the girls in the barn, who all gave us a friendly wave.

"So I did a bit of investigating and found that *they* caught a disease called cowpox from the cows they milked. Cowpox is like smallpox, but not nearly as serious. The maids caught it from touching the cowpox sores on the cows' udders but, rather than making them really poorly, it just made them a bit sick. And when they got over the cowpox they were no longer in danger from smallpox. That set me thinking and I decided to carry out a little experiment."

"And I was the one what he did it on," said the boy. "I'm James Phipps. My dad's *his* gardener."

"On 14 May 1796 I scraped pus from one of the sores on the arm of a milkmaid who'd got cowpox," said Dr Jenner. "And then I made scratches in James's arm and rubbed it in them."

"By 1 July, James seemed better so I decided it was time to test if he would now be resistant to smallpox."

"But he didn't know if it would work!" cried James.

"Yes, James," said Dr Jenner. "But it was for the good of all mankind. And you're here, aren't you? So stop whingeing!"

"After he done me, he tried it on 23 other people," said James.

"And it worked every time!" grinned Dr Jenner. "I knew I was on to something: a successful way of giving people complete protection from the dreaded smallpox. I've decided to name my new treatment after the cows that cowpox comes from."

THE LATIN WORD FOR COW IS "VACCA", SO I'M GOING TO CALL MY TREATMENT... VACCINATION!

"I'm hoping that my new vaccination procedure will soon be used throughout the country," said Dr Jenner. "It could save so many lives."

Then he looked unhappy and said, "Sadly, most doctors are still very suspicious of it and are refusing to use it. I do hope my efforts aren't to be for nothing!"

"Don't worry, Dr Jenner," said Mr Blood. "I bring you good news from the future. Soon, members of the Royal Family will hear of your new treatment and ask to be vaccinated. In a few years from now, you will receive £30,000 from the government to help you continue your great work!"

"But, Mr Blood, surely you are jesting?" said Dr Jenner, looking completely amazed.

"I'm not," said Mr Blood. "By the late 1800s vaccination will be both free and compulsory for every single child in Britain. Thousands of young lives will be saved! *And* vaccination will be used in other countries, too."

Dr Jenner and James were now looking at Mr Blood with their mouths open and their eyes as big as saucers.

"But here is the best news of all," continued Mr Blood. "In 200 years' time the scourge of smallpox will have been wiped from the face of the entire planet. All thanks to you,

Dr Jenner! And to you, James Phipps!"

Tears were now rolling down the cheeks of the doctor and the boy. Even Mr Blood's eyes had begun to go all wet and shiny.

"Better be off now, children," he sniffed. "More to do back at school!"

He gave Dr Jenner and James a farewell handshake and we all waved goodbye as a thick mist began rolling up around us. Moments later it cleared and we were all back in class.

THAT WAS TOTALLY BRILLIANT!

"Mr Blood?" I asked. "The cowpox triggered James's white blood cells to make antibodies – that's what saved him from the smallpox, wasn't it?"

"Exactly right, Laxmi. Well done!" he said beaming, and I blushed all over.

"So poor James was the first kid in the world ever to get the dreaded jab!" said Daniel.

"Yes, he was," said Mr Blood. "Except now you don't have your arm scratched like James did. You're vaccinated with a hypodermic needle like this."

He waved his giant syringe at us.

"Don't you mean you're *cow*-inated!" laughed Kelly!

"Ha! Very good, Kelly!" snorted Mr Blood. "We don't just get *cow*-inated for smallpox, these days. We have hypodermic jabs for all sorts of dangerous nasties including polio, malaria, tetanus and tuberculosis.

"We receive a dose of their germs that have been weakened with chemicals; just enough to get our white cells churning out the antibodies that will protect us from them should they strike for real at some time in the future."

"And hypodermic means under the skin," said Simon. "I've just looked it up."

"But why do we have to have the vaccine injected under our skin? Couldn't we just take it on a chocolate biscuit or something?" asked Daniel, licking his lips.

"Well, they do give vaccinations on a sugar lump in some countries," said Mr Blood. "But that way your digestive juices can destroy the vaccine before it gets a chance to enter the bloodstream."

"It's great that people like Dr Jenner have made it so we don't have to worry about things like smallpox any more," said Brian.

"Those great pioneers of medicine have certainly made the world a much safer place for us all," said Mr Blood. "The most important thing we have to do now is to stay healthy and look after our amazing bodies properly."

"And don't forget," said Mr Blood, "it's really important to get plenty of *brain* exercise, too."

"Well, Mr Blood's Body Lessons have certainly given us all tons of that!" said Daniel.

"Definitely!" said Kelly. "I think everything I've learned must have created thousands of new links between my brain cells."

"Me too!" said Simon. "I think I've probably got squillions of extra ones now!"

"Oh no!" I groaned. "Does that mean we've all got to start calling you Simon '*Four Brains*' Sidworth from now on?!"